Adolescent Relapse Prevention Workbook

A Brief Strategic Approach

Developed by

Terence T. Gorski

Based on The GORSKI-CENAPS® Model

The CENAPS® Corporation

Notice of Proprietary Information: This material is intended only for personal use of the person purchasing it. This document contains copyrighted and proprietary information of Terence T. Gorski and The CENAPS® Corporation. Its receipt or possession does not convey any right to reproduce it, or to manufacture, use or sell anything it may describe. Reproduction, disclosure, and use without the specific written authorization of Terence T. Gorski and The CENAPS® Corporation are strictly forbidden.

The Most Advanced Clinical Skills Training Available

ISBN 0-8309-0769-6

Adolescent Relapse Prevention Workbook

By Terence T. Gorski

Table of Contents

The Goals for This Workbook

Developed By Terence T. Gorski (© Copyright, Terence T. Gorski 1982, 1994)

THE CENAPS® CORPORATION   352/596-8000
6147 DelTona Blvd., Spring Hill, FL 34606   Fax: 352/596-8002

This workbook is designed for teens who have tried to recover from chemical dependency or the use of other self-defeating behaviors, but haven't been able to recover successfully. Some of you may have actually relapsed. Others are still in recovery but are having problems that make you think you might relapse in the future.

Your main goal in finishing the workbook is to learn how to stop your relapse pattern. You can do this by learning how to *identify* (recognize and name) and *manage* (cope with) your relapse warning signs. You also do it by working out a schedule of recovery activities that will support the warning sign identification and management that you'll have to keep working on if you want to stay in recovery.

To meet these goals you'll need to do more than just read and fill out this workbook. You'll need to talk about your answers to each exercise with another person who can help you sort out the thoughts and feelings that get stirred up by the exercises. This person needs to be a therapist trained in the GORSKI-CENAPS® Model of Relapse Prevention. (For a list of Certified Relapse Prevention Specialists, call or write to The CENAPS® Corporation.)

It's a good idea to also go to group sessions where each member is working through these exercises at the same time. *Talking about what you're learning from each exercise with another person or a group of people will make it easier for you to change in a way that will stop relapse.*

Here is the process that this workbook will lead you through:

1. **The Effects of Alcohol and Other Drugs:** You'll look at the kinds of things that alcohol and drugs did for you, and what you wanted to get from alcohol and drug use. (Look at Exercise 1)

2. **The Decision to Start Using:** You'll look at the reasons why you started using alcohol or other drugs. (Look at Exercise 2)

3. **Alcohol and Drug-Related Problems:** You'll identify the problems that you had because you were using alcohol and drugs. (Look at Exercise 3)

4. **The Decision to Stop Using:** You'll look into the reasons why you stopped using alcohol and drugs and what you did to stay clean and sober. (Look at Exercise 4)

5. **Warning Sign Identification:** You'll read a list of common relapse warning signs that lead from solid recovery to relapse, and find a personal warning sign that has happened to you. (Look at Exercise 5)

6. **Warning Sign Analysis:** You'll *analyze* (think about and come to understand) the warning sign you picked, by writing a personal title and a personal description that are easy for you to understand and remember. Then you'll identify the *irrational thoughts* (thoughts that seem to make sense but don't really), *unmanageable feelings* (feelings that are out of control), *self-destructive urges* (urges to do things that will hurt you), and *self-defeating behaviors* (words and actions that work against you) that drive the warning sign. (Look at Exercise 6)

7. **Situation Mapping:** You'll describe one past situation in which this warning sign came up for you in recovery and you didn't handle it very well. This situation will be used to help you to identify the pattern of self-defeating behaviors that drives the relapse process. This pattern is called a *self-reinforcing problem structure* because the effects of each problem lead to another problem, which leads to still another problem, until things get so bad that you can't stand it any more. Then you'll be asked to describe one past situation in which you experienced this warning sign in recovery and managed it well. You'll use this situation to find new and more effective ways of coping with the warning sign. (This is called identifying the *basic solution structure*.) These new ways of coping will be the foundation for Warning Sign Management and Recovery Planning. (Look at Exercise 7, Parts A and B)

8. **Thought Management:** You'll identify the irrational thoughts that drive the relapse warning sign you selected, and come up with new and more effective ways of thinking that will help you avoid relapse. (Look at Exercise 8)

9. **Feeling Management:** You'll identify the unmanageable feelings that drive the identified relapse warning sign, and come up with new and more effective ways of managing these feelings, which will help you avoid relapse. (Look at Exercise 9)

10. **Behavior and Situation Management:** You'll learn to identify the high-risk situations and self-defeating behaviors that drive the identified relapse warning sign by *mapping* a situation that occurred in the past, looking at exactly what happened and why. You'll learn to manage this kind of high-risk situation more effectively by finding three *intervention points*—points in the situation where you can use better ways of thinking, feeling, and acting to avoid relapse. Then you'll see how these new ways of coping might work in a future high-risk situation. (Look at Exercise 10)

11. **Recovery Planning:** You'll come up with a schedule of recovery activities that will help you keep on identifying and managing relapse warning signs. You'll write a schedule of recovery activities and figure out how you can work each activity to help you identify and manage your warning signs. (Look at Exercise 11)

12. **Overall Ability to Prevent Relapse:** You'll improve your overall ability to prevent relapse by learning how to identify and manage the warning signs that lead from stable recovery to alcohol and drug use. (Look at Exercise 12)

The Warning Sign Identification and Management process isn't easy. You'll have to work hard both during your sessions and on homework assignments between sessions. This can work for you if you come at it with an open mind and a willingness to work hard, learn some new and surprising things about yourself, and make changes.

At the end of this manual is an exercise that will help you take stock of how well you've done. Good luck!

Exercise 1: What Alcohol and Other Drugs Do

• Part 1: The Effects of Alcohol and Other Drugs

Alcohol and other drugs change how the brain and nervous system work. They either slow down, speed up, block out, change, or "blow up" the messages and feelings that our brain sends out to us. These drug effects make us feel different for a little while, but they don't really change anything in the real world. They change how we think and feel, but they don't make our lives any better.

Drugs can be grouped by how they make us feel and what we want them to do for us. Below is a description of the six most common things people want drugs to do, the feelings that the drugs bring that make them believe they're getting what they want, and the common drugs of choice that bring on those effects.

Alcohol and other drugs are sometimes called *mood-altering substances*. That's because they change the way we feel. People use these drugs to get a certain *effect* (result) that they think is desirable. There are basically six types of effects that people want to get from using alcohol and drugs. These are:

1. **Social Lubrication:** If I'm using alcohol or other drugs for *social lubrication* (to make things easier for me socially), the effect that I want is to feel like I fit in, and to feel like I can party and have fun with my friends. The main drugs that give me this effect are alcohol and marijuana.

2. **Relaxation:** If I'm using alcohol or other drugs for relaxation, the effect I want to get is to feel relaxed and mellow. The main drugs that give me this effect are *downers,* like alcohol, sleeping pills, or tranquilizers.

3. **Stimulation:** If I'm using alcohol or other drugs for stimulation, the effect I want to get is to feel "up" — stimulated, energized, or excited. The main drugs that give me this effect are caffeine, amphetamines (speed), and cocaine.

4. **Blocking Out Pain:** If I'm using alcohol or other drugs to block out feelings of pain, I want the drugs to help me block out or get away from painful feelings or emotions. The main drugs that give me this effect are *narcotic pain killers* like codeine, Demerol, morphine, or heroin.

5. **Altered States of Consciousness:** If I'm using alcohol or other drugs for altered states of consciousness, I might want to feel more spiritual or like I've been lifted to a higher part of my mind. Or I might just want to get silly and watch the wallpaper move around. The main drugs that give me this effect are *hallucinogens* or mind benders like marijuana (pot), hashish, ecstasy, LSD, or PCP.

6. **Managing Feelings:** If I'm using alcohol or other drugs to manage my feelings, I want the drugs to help me recognize and deal with my feelings better. Sometimes I need to take the edge off very strong feelings. At other times I think I need the drugs to give me the courage to face what I'm feeling or to tell others about my feelings. At still other times I want to turn off my feelings for a little while so I can think about or focus on other things.

Exercise 1: What Alcohol and Other Drugs Do

- ## Part 2: Using Alcohol and Other Drugs for Social Lubrication

> *Desired Effect:*   I want to party and have fun with my friends.

1.   Tell a story you've heard about someone who used some kind of mood-altering substance for social lubrication.

_____

_____

_____

_____

_____

_____

_____

_____

2.   Can you think of three problems a teenager might have that could make him or her want to use alcohol or other drugs for social lubrication?

Problem #1: _____

_____

_____

_____

Problem #2: _____

_____

_____

_____

Problem #3: _____

_____

_____

_____

Exercise 1:   What Alcohol and Other Drugs Do

• Part 3: Using Alcohol and Other Drugs for Relaxation

> *Desired Effect:*   I want to relax and feel mellow.

1.   Tell a story you've heard about someone who used some kind of mood-altering substance for relaxation.

_____

_____

_____

_____

_____

_____

_____

2.   Can you think of three problems that a teenager might have that could make him or her want to use alcohol or other drugs for relaxation?

Problem #1: _____

_____

_____

_____

Problem #2: _____

_____

_____

_____

Problem #3: _____

_____

_____

_____

Exercise 1:   What Alcohol and Other Drugs Do

• Part 4: Using Alcohol and Other Drugs for Stimulation

> *Desired Effect:*   I want to feel "up" and get more energy and excitement.

1.   Tell a story you've heard about someone who used some kind of mood-altering substance for stimulation.

_____

_____

_____

_____

2.   Can you think of three problems that a teenager might have that could make him or her want to use alcohol or other drugs for stimulation?

Problem #1: _____

_____

_____

_____

_____

Problem #2: _____

_____

_____

_____

_____

Problem #3: _____

_____

_____

_____

_____

Exercise 1: What Alcohol and Other Drugs Do

• Part 5: Using Alcohol and Other Drugs to Block Out Pain

> *Desired Effect:* I want to numb out and block out reality.

1. Tell a story you've heard about someone who used some kind of mood-altering substance for blocking out painful feelings.

   _____

   _____

   _____

   _____

   _____

2. Can you think of three problems that a teenager might have that could make him or her want to use alcohol or other drugs to block out painful feelings?

   Problem #1: _____

   _____

   _____

   _____

   _____

   Problem #2: _____

   _____

   _____

   _____

   _____

   Problem #3: _____

   _____

   _____

   _____

   _____

Exercise 1:   What Alcohol and Other Drugs Do

• Part 6: Using Alcohol and Other Drugs to Alter States of Consciousness

> *Desired Effect:*   I want to alter my state of consciousness
> and have spiritual or transcendental experiences.

1.   Tell a story you've heard about someone who used some kind of mood-altering substance to have altered states of consciousness.

   _____

   _____

   _____

   _____

   _____

2.   Can you think of three problems a teenager might have that could make him or her want to use alcohol or other drugs to have altered states of consciousness?

   Problem #1: _____

   _____

   _____

   _____

   _____

   Problem #2: _____

   _____

   _____

   _____

   Problem #3: _____

   _____

   _____

   _____

   _____

Exercise 1:   What Alcohol and Other Drugs Do

• Part 7: Using Alcohol and Other Drugs to Manage Feelings

Desired Effect:	I want to manage my feelings and emotions more effectively.

1. Tell a story you've heard about someone who used some kind of mood-altering substance to manage feelings more effectively.

    _____

    _____

    _____

    _____

    _____

2. Can you think of three problems that a teenager might have that could make him or her want to use alcohol or other drugs to manage feelings more effectively?

    Problem #1: _____

    _____

    _____

    _____

    _____

    Problem #2: _____

    _____

    _____

    _____

    _____

    Problem #3: _____

    _____

    _____

    _____

    _____

Exercise 1:   What Alcohol and Other Drugs Do

• Part 8:   What I Wanted Alcohol and Other Drugs to Do for Me

1. What are the three most important things you wanted alcohol or other drugs to do for you?

    A. _____

    B. _____

    C. _____

2. Can you do these things for yourself without using alcohol or other drugs?

    ☐ Yes ☐ No ☐ Unsure   Please explain: _____

    _____

    _____

3. What are the three most important things you wanted alcohol or other drugs to help you cope with or escape from?

    A. _____

    _____

    B. _____

    _____

    C. _____

    _____

4. Can you cope with or escape from these things without using alcohol or other drugs?

    ☐ Yes ☐ No ☐ Unsure   Please explain: _____

    _____

    _____

5. Looking back on it now, do you think that the alcohol and other drugs did for you what you wanted them to do? ☐ Yes   ☐ No   ☐ Unsure

    Please explain your answer: _____

    _____

    _____

    _____

    _____

Exercise 2:   Why I Decided to Start Using

- ## Part 1: The Story of the First Time I Used Alcohol

Instructions: Go back in your mind to the first time you made the decision to start drinking alcoholic beverages (beer, wine, wine coolers, mixed drinks, or liquor).

1.   Briefly tell the story of the first time you used alcohol, why you decided to use it, and what happened as a result.

The first time I used alcohol was . . . _____

_____

_____

_____

_____

_____

_____

_____

The reason I decided to use it was . . . _____

_____

_____

_____

_____

_____

_____

_____

The things that happened to me as a result of using it were . . . _____

_____

_____

_____

_____

_____

_____

_____

2. What did you want the alcohol to do for you?

_____

_____

3. What did you want alcohol to help you cope with o r escape from?

_____

_____

4. What are the most important reasons you decided to start using alcohol?

_____

_____

_____

5. What are the three most important fears you had when you thought about using alcohol?

A. _____

_____

B. _____

_____

C. _____

_____

6. What are the three main things you did to get over those fears and talk yourself into using alcohol?

A. _____

_____

B. _____

_____

C. _____

_____

7. What good things did you get because you used alcohol?

_____

_____

_____

8. What problems or bad things happened because you used alcohol?

_____

_____

_____

Exercise 2:   Why I Decided to Start Using

• Part 2: The Story of the First Time I Used Drugs

Instructions: I want you to go back in your mind to the first time that you made the decision to start using drugs.

1.   Briefly tell the story of the first time you used drugs, why you decided to use it, and what happened as a result.

The first time I used drugs was . . . _____

_____

_____

_____

_____

_____

_____

_____

_____

The reason I decided to use it was . . . _____

_____

_____

_____

_____

_____

_____

_____

The things that happened to me as a result of using it were . . . _____

_____

_____

_____

_____

_____

_____

_____

2. What did you want the drugs to do for you?

_____

_____

3. What did you want drugs to help you cope with or escape from?

_____

_____

4. What are the most important reasons you decided to start using drugs?

_____

_____

_____

5. What are the three most important fears you had when you thought about using drugs?
   A. _____

   _____

   B. _____

   _____

   C. _____

   _____

6. What are the three main things you did to get over those fears and talk yourself into using drugs?
   A. _____

   _____

   B. _____

   _____

   C. _____

   _____

7. What good things did you get because you used drugs?

_____

_____

_____

8. What problems or bad things happened because you used drugs?

_____

_____

_____

Exercise 3:   What Happened after I Started to Use

• Part 1: How Alcohol and Drug Use Affected My Development

Instructions: The regular and heavy use of alcohol and drugs can slow down or stop the normal process of development (physical, mental, and emotional growth) in adolescence. The following questions will help you think about the normal tasks of adolescent development and how alcohol and drugs may have affected your ability to finish those tasks.

There are a series of primary tasks that you need to complete to move through adolescence and become a responsible adult. These are:

1. **Being able to think clearly:** This involves being able to learn things, figure things out, and solve problems.

    A.   How has using alcohol and drugs helped you think more clearly?

    _____

    _____

    B.   How has using alcohol and drugs kept you from thinking more clearly

    _____

    _____

    C.   If you had to stop using alcohol and drugs, how would it affect your ability to think clearly?

    _____

    _____

2. **Managing your feelings and emotions:** This involves being able to recognize when you are having a feeling, accurately describing the feeling in words, telling others about your feelings, dealing with painful feelings, and making yourself feel good feelings.

    A.   How has using alcohol and drugs helped you learn how to manage your feelings and emotions?

    _____

    _____

    B.   How has using alcohol and drugs kept you from effectively managing your feelings and emotions?

    _____

    _____

    C.   If you had to stop using alcohol and drugs, how would it affect your ability to manage your feelings and emotions?

    _____

    _____

    _____

3. **Controlling your impulses and urges:** This involves being able to stop yourself from doing things that are not good for you even if you really want to do them.

A. How has using alcohol and drugs helped you control your impulses?

_____

_____

_____

B. How has using alcohol and drugs kept you from controlling your impulses?

_____

_____

_____

C. If you had to stop using alcohol and drugs, how would it affect your ability to control your impulses?

_____

_____

_____

4. **Overcoming your resistance to grow and change:** This involves being able to motivate yourself to do unpleasant things that are good for you even if you don't really want to do them.

A. How has using alcohol and drugs helped you overcome your resistance to grow and change?

_____

_____

_____

B. How has using alcohol and drugs kept you from overcoming your resistance to grow and change?

_____

_____

_____

C. If you had to stop using alcohol and drugs, how would it affect your ability to overcome your resistance to grow and change?

_____

_____

_____

5.   **Developing your own identity as an individual:** This involves figuring out who you are and how you're different from others.

   A.   How has using alcohol and drugs helped you establish an identity as an individual that you can be proud of?

   _____

   _____

   _____

   B.   How has using alcohol and drugs kept you from establishing an identity as an individual that you can be proud of?

   _____

   _____

   _____

   C.   If you had to stop using alcohol and drugs, how would it affect your identity as an individual?

   _____

   _____

   _____

6.   **Being able to do things on your own without getting into trouble:** This involves building friendships and activities that are separate from those of your parents and your family.

   A.   How has using alcohol and drugs helped you do things on your own without getting into trouble?

   _____

   _____

   _____

   B.   How has using alcohol and drugs kept you from doing things on your own without getting into trouble?

   _____

   _____

   _____

   C.   If you had to stop using alcohol and drugs, how would it affect your ability to do things on your own without getting into trouble?

   _____

   _____

   _____

7. **Being able to take care of yourself:** This involves being able to support yourself financially and emotionally without having to rely too much on the help of your parents or other people.

   A.   How has using alcohol and drugs helped you learn how to take care of yourself without having to rely too much on other people?

   _____

   _____

   _____

   B.   How has using alcohol and drugs kept you from learning how to take care of yourself without having to rely too much on other people?

   _____

   _____

   _____

   C.   If you had to stop using alcohol and drugs, how would it affect your ability to take care of yourself without having to rely too much on other people?

   _____

   _____

   _____

8. **Using your strengths to help others:** This involves being able to use your strengths and talents to help and support others when they need it.

   A.   How has using alcohol and drugs helped you learn how to help others more effectively?

   _____

   _____

   _____

   B.   How has using alcohol and drugs kept you from learning how to help others more effectively?

   _____

   _____

   _____

   C.   If you had to stop using alcohol and drugs, how would it affect your ability to help others?

   _____

   _____

   _____

9. **Being able to receive help from others:** This involves being able to ask for and accept help and support from others when you need it.

    A.   How has using alcohol and drugs helped you learn how to ask for and accept help and support from others?

    _____

    _____

    _____

    B.   How has using alcohol and drugs kept you from asking for and accepting help and support from others?

    _____

    _____

    _____

    C.   If you had to stop using alcohol and drugs, how would it affect your ability to ask for and accept help and support from others?

    _____

    _____

    _____

10. **Being able to become a responsible adult:** This involves being able to gain the respect of other adults and establish yourself as their equal.

    A.   How has using alcohol and drugs helped you become a responsible adult?

    _____

    _____

    _____

    B.   How has using alcohol and drugs kept you from becoming a responsible adult?

    _____

    _____

    _____

    C.   If you had to stop using alcohol and drugs, how would it affect your ability to become a responsible adult?

    _____

    _____

    _____

Exercise 3: What Happened after I Started to Use

• Part 2: Rating Your Current Adolescent Development

1. **Self-Evaluation of Current Development:** Review your evaluation of the 10 key areas of adolescent development and evaluate your current level of development. Place your rating of your current level of development (0 – 10) on the blank line in front of each area.

<table>
<tr><td colspan="3" align="center">Rating Scale</td></tr>
<tr><td>0</td><td>=</td><td>I have not yet begun to develop in this area.</td></tr>
<tr><td>5</td><td>=</td><td>I have developed some capabilities in this area
but I still need to develop others.</td></tr>
<tr><td>10</td><td>=</td><td>I have fully developed all the capabilities in this area.</td></tr>
</table>

___ 1. Being able to think clearly: Why did you rate yourself that way?

_____

___ 2. Managing your feelings and emotions: Why did you rate yourself that way?

_____

___ 3. Controlling your impulses and urges: Why did you rate yourself that way?

_____

___ 4. Overcoming your resistance to grow and change: Why did you rate yourself that way?

_____

___ 5. Developing your own identity as an individual: Why did you rate yourself that way?

_____

___ 6. Being able to do things on your own without getting into trouble: Why did you rate yourself that way?

_____

___ 7. Being able to take care of yourself: Why did you rate yourself that way?

_____

___ 8. Using your strengths to help others: Why did you rate yourself that way?

_____

___ 9. Being able to receive help from others: Why did you rate yourself that way?

_____

___ 10. Being able to become a responsible adult: Why did you rate yourself that way?

_____

2. What are the three most important ways that using alcohol and drugs has helped you to develop the skills you will need to be an effective adult?

A. _____

_____

B. _____

_____

C. _____

_____

3. Could you have developed in these ways without using alcohol or drugs?

☐ Yes ☐ No ☐ Unsure Please explain: _____

_____

_____

4. What are the three most important ways that using alcohol and drugs has caused you problems in developing the skills you will need to be an effective adult?

A. _____

_____

B. _____

_____

C. _____

_____

5. If you didn't use alcohol and drugs do you think you would have had the same problems developing the skills you will need to be an effective adult?

☐ Yes ☐ No ☐ Unsure Please explain: _____

_____

_____

6. Looking back on it now, do you think that the alcohol and drugs did for you what you wanted them to do? ☐ Yes ☐ No ☐ Unsure

Please explain your answer: _____

_____

_____

_____

_____

Exercise 3:   What Happened after I Started to Use

• Part 3: The Alcohol and Drug Problem Checklist

Instructions: Sometimes when people start to use alcohol and other drugs they begin to have problems. These problems are often described as the *symptoms* of addiction or chemical dependency. Answer each question below as honestly as you can. The more questions that you answer yes to, the more likely it is that you're suffering from chemical dependency.

You may notice that some of the questions will make you uncomfortable. As a matter of fact, you may notice that you have an urge to lie about your answers. If this happens, it means that you have an urge to deny the problems related to your use of alcohol and other drugs. This is definitely a sign that something is wrong. You should talk to your counselor about the questions that cause an urge to lie.

The goal of having you answer these questions is to give you a chance to think about some of the problems that you may be having. To make these questions helpful for you, you need to take the time to think about and talk about your answers. You also need to notice the feelings that each question stirs up. Some of these questions may raise concerns in your own mind, or may make you start arguing with yourself in your own head. These are questions that you need to talk about with someone else.

☐ Yes ☐ No   1. Have you ever used alcohol without your parents?

☐ Yes ☐ No   2. Do you usually use alcohol more than twice a month?

☐ Yes ☐ No   3. On the days when you use alcohol, do you usually have three drinks or more?

☐ Yes ☐ No   4. On the days when you use alcohol, do you usually drink heavily and want to get drunk?

☐ Yes ☐ No   5. If you couldn't use alcohol because of a medical problem, do you think that it would it be difficult for you to stop?

☐ Yes ☐ No   6. If you use mood-altering drugs that have been prescribed for you by your doctor, do you sometimes use more than the amount prescribed, or use them at times your doctor didn't tell you to use them?

☐ Yes ☐ No   7. Do you sometimes use mood-altering drugs that have been prescribed for someone else? (This could happen when your parents, brothers or sisters, or friends share some of their prescribed medications.)

☐ Yes ☐ No   8. Do you ever use any other drugs that aren't prescribed for you by your doctor? (These might be medicines like diet pills, sleep aids, stay-awake pills, or herbal energy supplements that make you high or give you a buzz. It might also include street drugs that you buy from friends or other people.)

☐ Yes ☐ No 9. Do you get *intoxicated* (drunk or high) on alcohol or drugs more than twice a year? (You're drunk or high if you use so much that you can't function safely or normally, or if other people think you can't function safely or normally.)

☐ Yes ☐ No 10. When you're using alcohol or drugs, do you ever put yourself in situations that raise your risk of getting hurt, having problems, or hurting others? (This includes things like driving while using alcohol or drugs, having sex without protection, getting into fights, skipping school, committing crimes, etc.)

☐ Yes ☐ No 11. Do you ever brag about your ability to drink heavily or use a lot of drugs?

☐ Yes ☐ No 12. Have you ever felt that you should cut down on your drinking or drug use?

☐ Yes ☐ No 13. Have your parents, teachers, or other adults ever been annoyed by or criticized you because of your drinking or drug use?

☐ Yes ☐ No 14. Have your friends ever been annoyed by or criticized you because of your drinking or drug use?

☐ Yes ☐ No 15. Have you ever put yourself down or criticized yourself because of your alcohol or drug use, or because of something that happened while you were drinking or drugging?

☐ Yes ☐ No 16. Have you ever lost a friend because that friend didn't like your alcohol or drug use?

☐ Yes ☐ No 17. Have you ever stopped seeing a friend you used to like because that friend wouldn't drink or use drugs with you?

☐ Yes ☐ No 18. Have you ever felt bad or guilty about your drinking or using drugs?

☐ Yes ☐ No 19. Have you ever done things while you were using alcohol or drugs that you regretted or that made you feel guilty or ashamed?

☐ Yes ☐ No 20. Have you ever used alcohol or drugs first thing in the morning to feel better, get rid of a hangover, or get ready to face the day?

☐ Yes ☐ No 21. Have you ever used alcohol or drugs to try to escape from or cope with a problem or situation that you didn't know any other way to deal with?

☐ Yes ☐ No 22. Have you ever thought that you might have a problem with your drinking or drug use?

☐ Yes ☐ No 23. Has anyone else (a parent, brother, sister, teacher, or friend) ever told you that they thought you might have a problem with your drinking or drug use?

☐ Yes ☐ No 24. Do you ever use alcohol or drugs in larger quantities than you planned to (for example, you use more than you want to or can afford to)?

☐ Yes ☐ No 25. Do you ever use alcohol or drugs more often than you planned to (for example, you plan not to use today but you do it anyway)?

☐ Yes ☐ No 26. Do you ever use alcohol or drugs for longer periods of time than you planned to (for example, you can't stop when you planned to)?

☐ Yes ☐ No 27. Have you ever had a desire to cut down or control your use?

☐ Yes ☐ No 28. Have you ever actually tried to cut down or control your use?

☐ Yes ☐ No 29. Are you spending more and more time planning to use, or actually using alcohol or drugs?

☐ Yes ☐ No 30. Have you ever failed to finish your schoolwork because you were using alcohol or drugs or feeling hung over?

☐ Yes ☐ No 31. Have you ever failed to do the things you were supposed to do at home because you were using alcohol or drugs or feeling hung over?

☐ Yes ☐ No 32. Have you ever let other people down whom you cared about because you were using alcohol or drugs or feeling hung over?

☐ Yes ☐ No 33. Have you given up any work, social, or recreational activities because of alcohol or drug use?

☐ Yes ☐ No 34. Have you ever gotten in trouble with the police as a result of what happened when you were using alcohol or drugs?

☐ Yes ☐ No 35. Have you ever had problems or conflicts at home because of your use of alcohol or drugs?

☐ Yes ☐ No 36. Have your parents ever punished you because of something that happened when you were using alcohol or drugs?

☐ Yes ☐ No 37. Have you ever been too sick to go to school as a result of using alcohol or drugs? (This includes bad hangovers.)

☐ Yes ☐ No 38. Have you ever missed school in order to hang out with your friends who use alcohol and drugs, or to do things that involve alcohol or drug use?

☐ Yes ☐ No 39. Have you ever had problems or conflicts at school because of your use of alcohol or drugs?

☐ Yes ☐ No 40. Have you ever gotten into trouble at school because of things that happened when you were using alcohol or drugs? (This includes being disciplined, getting detentions, being sent to the person in charge of discipline, having your parents notified of problems, or being suspended.)

☐ Yes ☐ No 41. Have you ever had problems with friends as a result of your use of alcohol or drugs?

☐ Yes ☐ No 42. Have you ever gotten physically sick as a result of your alcohol or drug use?

☐ Yes ☐ No 43. Have you ever kept on using alcohol or drugs even though you knew they were causing problems or making your problems worse?

☐ Yes ☐ No 44. Has your tolerance (your ability to use a lot of alcohol and drugs without feeling drunk or high) gotten higher since you started to use?

☐ Yes ☐ No 45. Do you have to use more alcohol or drugs in order to get the same effect you used to get when you used less?

☐ Yes ☐ No 46. Do you ever get physically uncomfortable or sick on the day after using alcohol or drugs?

☐ Yes ☐ No 47. Have you ever used alcohol or drugs to keep from getting sick the next day or to make a hangover go away?

☐ Yes ☐ No 48. Has a doctor or a therapist ever told you that he or she thought you had a serious problem with alcohol or drugs?

☐ Yes ☐ No 49. Have you ever sold alcohol or drugs to other kids who had trouble getting them for themselves?

☐ Yes ☐ No 50. Did you feel uncomfortable or have the urge to lie when answering any of the above questions?

Exercise 3:   What Happened after I Started to Use

• Part 4: Interpreting the Alcohol and Drug Problem Checklist

1. Count how many times you answered "Yes" to any of the questions numbered 1 through 10.

    How many "Yes" answers did you check? _____

2. Count how many times you answered "Yes" to any of the questions numbered 11 through 50.

    How many "Yes" answers did you check? _____

3. Check the box below that most accurately describes your risk of addiction based on your answers to *The Alcohol and Drug Problem Checklist.*

    A. **Low Risk for Addiction:** If you answered "No" to all of the above questions you are at a low risk for addiction.

    B. **High Risk for Addiction:** If you answered "Yes" to three or more of the questions numbered 1 through 10 and answered "No" to all the remaining questions you are at a high risk of becoming addicted.

    C. **Early Stage Addiction:** If you answered "Yes" to three or more of the questions numbered 1 through 10 and answered "Yes" to between three and six of the questions numbered 11 through 50 you are probably in the early stages of addiction.

    D. **Middle Stage Addiction:** If you answered "Yes" to three or more of the questions numbered 1 through 10 and answered "Yes" to between seven and ten of the questions numbered 11 through 50 you are probably in the middle stages of addiction.

    E. **Late Stage Addiction:** If you answered "Yes" to three or more of the questions numbered 1 through 10 and answered "Yes" to eleven or more of the questions numbered 11 through 50 you are probably in the late stages of addiction.

4. If you believe that alcohol and drugs can do things for you that you can't do without them you are probably psychologically or socially dependent on alcohol or drugs to learn new things and to grow emotionally.

5. If you believe that alcohol and drugs can help cope with or escape from things that you can't without them you are probably psychologically or socially dependent on alcohol or drugs to cope with pain and to solve problems.

6. Do you believe that the results of *The Alcohol and Drug Problem Checklist* accurately describe your current risk of addiction to alcohol and drugs?

    ☐ Yes ☐ No ☐ Unsure   Please explain your answer: _____

    _____

    _____

    _____

Exercise 4: Why I Decided to Stop Using

- ## Part 1: The Benefits and Disadvantages of Alcohol and Drug Use

1. **Benefits:** List the main things that were better for you because you used alcohol and other drugs.	2. **Disadvantages:** List the main things that were worse for you, or problems that you had because you used alcohol and drugs.

3. Looking back on it, do you think that the benefits you got from using alcohol and drugs were worth the pain and problems that you experienced? ☐ Yes ☐ No ☐ Unsure

Please explain your answer: _____

_____

_____

_____

Exercise 4:   Why I Decided to Stop Using

• Part 2: The Reasons Why I Stopped

Instructions: Read each statement below and put a check mark in front of the ones that apply to you.

The main reasons why I decided to stop using alcohol and other drugs were...

☐ 1. **People in authority made me stop.** I really didn't want to stop, but I got caught using alcohol or drugs and my parents or teachers made me stop.

☐ 2. **I didn't like the problems.** I didn't get caught, but I knew that I was starting to have problems as a result of using alcohol and drugs. I could see that the problems were getting worse, so I decided to stop before I did get caught.

☐ 3. **I didn't like the effects.** I decided to stop using alcohol and other drugs because I didn't like how they made me feel. Either I got sick while using or I felt sick the day after using.

☐ 4. **I realized it wasn't working.** I decided to stop because I knew that the alcohol and drug use wasn't giving me what I wanted to get.

☐ 5. **I didn't want to take the risks.** I decided to stop because I knew that using alcohol or drugs could make me sick or cause me to get into trouble, so I decided to stop in order not to have those problems.

☐ 6. **I realized it was the wrong thing to do.** I decided to stop because I realized that it was wrong to use alcohol and drugs and I wanted to do the right thing.

☐ 7. **Other Reasons:** The other reasons I decided to stop are...

_____

_____

_____

_____

Exercise 4:   Why I Decided to Stop Using

•   Part 3:   What I Did to Stay Sober

Instructions: Read the following statements and check the ones that apply to you.

The main things I did to keep myself from using alcohol and drugs were ...

1.   **Keeping myself busy with other things.** I kept myself busy doing other things so I wouldn't think about using alcohol or drugs.

    How helpful was this in your efforts to stay off alcohol and drugs?

    ☐ It helped a lot. ☐ It helped a little. ☐ It didn't help very much.

2.   **Avoiding my friends who used alcohol and drugs**. I stayed away from people I knew who used alcohol and drugs.

    How helpful was this in your efforts to stay off alcohol and drugs?

    ☐ It helped a lot. ☐ It helped a little. ☐ It didn't help very much.

3.   **Hanging out with people who didn't use alcohol or drugs.** I made friends with people who didn't use alcohol and drugs and I spent time with them.

    How helpful was this in your efforts to stay off alcohol and drugs?

    ☐ It helped a lot. ☐ It helped a little. ☐ It didn't help very much.

4.   **Going into a counseling or treatment program.** I went to see a counselor or I got into a counseling or treatment program that could help me stay away from alcohol and drugs.

    How helpful was this in your efforts to stay off alcohol and drugs?

    ☐ It helped a lot. ☐ It helped a little. ☐ It didn't help very much.

5.   **Going to self-help groups.** I started going to self-help groups like Alcoholics Anonymous (AA), Narcotics Anonymous (NA), or other groups that support sober and responsible living.

    How helpful was this in your efforts to stay off alcohol and drugs?

    ☐ It helped a lot. ☐ It helped a little. ☐ It didn't help very much.

7.   **Family Counseling.** I went into a family counseling program to learn how to deal with the problems I have with my parents and brothers and sisters that make me want to drink and use drugs.

    How helpful was this in your efforts to stay off alcohol and drugs?

    ☐ It helped a lot. ☐ It helped a little. ☐ It didn't help very much.

8.   **Other Things:** The other things I did to help myself stay off alcohol and other drugs were...

    _____

    _____

    _____

Exercise 5: Warning Sign Identification

• Part 1: The Adolescent Relapse Warning Sign List

Developed by Terence T. Gorski (© Copyright, Terence T. Gorski 1982, 1994)

THE CENAPS® CORPORATION   352/596-8000
6147 DelTona Blvd., Spring Hill, FL 34606   Fax: 352/596-8002

Instructions: This list of relapse warning signs can help you see how your problems lead from one to another, taking you from a comfortable and stable recovery back to relapse. It was developed based on the experience of many people who have had a hard time recovering.*

Please read the list carefully as a homework assignment between sessions. After you read each paragraph, stop for a minute or so and notice what you're thinking and feeling. Put a check mark (✔) next to any warning sign that you've experienced. Put a question mark (?) next to any warning sign you have a hard time understanding. Put an asterisk (*) next to any warning sign that makes you get upset or "space out" while you're reading it. At the next session with your therapist, please be ready to talk about the warning signs that stood out to you.

1. **Changing on the Inside:** I start to feel bad, but I can't figure out what's going wrong. I'm not drinking or using drugs. I'm looking good on the outside by doing what I'm supposed to do to stay off alcohol and drugs. I'm feeling bad on the inside because sobriety isn't what I thought it would be. I start to get frustrated and angry because my parents or teachers aren't giving me the credit I deserve for staying off alcohol and drugs. I notice that I'm falling back into old ways of thinking and managing feelings that I used to use when I was drinking and drugging. I'm worried about myself, but I don't know what's wrong.

2. **Lying to Myself:** I feel bad. I try to make the bad feelings go away by telling myself that everything's OK, when I know it really isn't. Sometimes I believe my own lies and feel better for a little while. At other times I know I'm lying, and I feel guilty about it. At still other times I'm confused and I can't tell whether I'm lying to myself or telling the truth. I tell myself I don't have to worry because I'll never relapse. I feel better, turn off my mind, and convince myself that everything is OK.

3. **Looking Good to Others:** I want to look good to others, so I hold back on what I'm really thinking or feeling. I start lying and covering up, instead of telling the truth and taking a chance on looking bad. I start playing a role that I think other people will like and accept. I tell everyone that everything is great when it really isn't. I start criticizing and putting others down in order to make myself look better than they are.

---

* I developed the first list of relapse warning signs based on the experience of clients who had relapsed many times. Then Tammy Bell and I changed the list to fit the experiences of teens who had relapse problems for her book *Preventing Adolescent Relapse* and her pamphlet *Adolescent Relapse Warning Signs*. Then I re-adapted the warning sign list to fit the brief therapy format used in this workbook.

4. **Feeling Like No One Wants to Be My Friend:** I want to fit in and have an exciting social life and a lot of good friends, but being clean and sober starts to get in the way. I feel ashamed and embarrassed that I can't drink or use drugs. I feel left out, because it seems like everyone else is drinking and drugging. It seems like the people I want to be friends with aren't interested in me because I can't drink or use drugs. When I have problems with my friends, I blame it on the fact that I can't drink or use drugs. I start to think that if only I could drink or use drugs, everything else would get better.

5. **Feeling Romantically Undesirable:** I want to have exciting romantic relationships, but I start to feel like this will never happen because I can't drink or use drugs. I start holding back when I'm around people I'm attracted to. I think possible romantic partners won't be interested in me because I can't drink or use drugs. When I have problems in my romantic relationships I blame it on the fact that I can't drink or use drugs. I start to think that if only I could drink or use drugs, everything else would get better.

6. **Convincing Myself That Adults Can't Help Me:** I convince myself that my parents, counselors, and teachers don't really understand me. I stop paying attention to what they're telling me. I start to believe that I'm smarter than they are. I look for every little thing they do that I don't like, and I use these things to convince myself that they're not on my side or that they're out to get me. I use this as an excuse to stop being honest with them. I know that if I tell them what I'm really thinking and feeling, they'll give me a hard time. And besides, it's none of their business.

7. **Staying Away from Friends Who Can Help:** I avoid people who will force me to be honest with myself, and this means staying away from my friends who are clean and sober. When I do talk to them, I tell them what they want to hear to keep them off my back. If they ask questions, give me feedback, or confront me, I get defensive, I can't hear what they're trying to tell me, or I tell them to leave me alone.

8. **Hanging Out with Old Friends Who Can't Help:** I feel like being with my old friends who are drinking and drugging. I convince myself that I can have a good time with them and get my mind off things. They seem to understand and support me. It seems like nobody else does.

9. **Feeling Bad That I Can't Party:** I start feeling bad that I can't drink and use drugs. I start to envy the other kids who can. I think that I'm missing out on a lot of fun and action. I start remembering and exaggerating all the good times I had when I was drinking and drugging. I minimize or block out most of the pain and problems. I start thinking about all the things I have to do to stay sober, and I make myself feel worse by thinking about how awful and terrible it is that I have to do those things and that I can't party and have fun like a "normal" person.

10. **Getting Compulsive:** I start using compulsive behaviors to keep my mind off how uncomfortable I am. Maybe I get so involved in dating, scoring, or making my relationships work that I lose touch with everything else. Maybe I watch too much TV. I eat too much, gain weight, and then starve myself to try and lose it. Maybe I drink too much coffee or too many soft drinks with caffeine in them. Maybe I smoke too many cigarettes. If I'm into sports, I practice too hard and train too much. If I'm into music, I practice my instrument too much and try to lose myself and my problems in my music.

11. **Acting Out:** I start doing some things that I'm not supposed to be doing, but I cover it up and get away with it. This gives me the courage to break bigger rules and to take bigger risks. I start to get reckless, use poor judgment, and impulsively do things without thinking them through. This "acting-out" behavior makes me feel important and powerful, but it drives sober and responsible people away while attracting people who drink, use drugs, and act out in dangerous ways.

12. **Crisis Building:** Things keep going wrong. I overreact to or mismanage each problem in a way that creates a new and bigger problem. No matter how hard I try, nothing seems to work. Two new problems seem to pop up to replace every problem I solve. I start having the same kinds of problems with school, friends, family, and money that I used to have before I got into recovery. I feel like nothing is going my way and that there's nothing I can do to solve the problems.

13. **Getting Defensive:** When people point out problems that I don't want to see, I get defensive, scared, and angry. I blame them for making me feel bad. I take the focus off myself by criticizing them, instead of honestly looking at my own problems. I end up driving people away. When people confront me I feel like they're expecting too much of me. I start to think, "What more do they want? I'm doing everything I can and it's not enough. Why bother?"

14. **Avoiding Family Members:** I stop doing things with my family. I make excuses to stay away from my mother, father, brothers, sisters, and other family members. I stop eating meals with the family. I refuse to go to family gatherings. I don't want to get involved in family parties. I think they're stupid and I'd rather be by myself. When I don't go, I feel left out and convince myself that no one in my family really cares about me. I get angry and tell myself that they don't count and I need to look out for number one.

15. **Getting Lonely:** I start spending more time alone. I usually have good reasons and excuses for staying away from other people. I start feeling lonely. Instead of dealing with the loneliness by trying to meet and be around other people, I start doing more things alone.

16. **Getting Depressed:** I get so depressed that I can't do the things I normally do. I feel like life isn't worth living, and sometimes I think about killing myself or relapsing as a way to end the depression. I stop eating right. I can't get started or get anything done. I sleep fitfully and almost never have a deep, relaxing sleep. I can't stick to my daily schedule. I isolate myself and convince myself that nobody cares and that there's no one who can help me. I feel trapped with no way out.

17. **Getting Immobilized:** I can't seem to get started or make myself do what I know I need to do. I stop following a daily routine. I stop getting up and going to bed at regular times. I start skipping meals and eating at unusual times. I find it hard to get to school on time. I stop doing homework and stop showing up for extra-curricular events at school. I sometimes cut classes or don't show up at school at all. I feel rushed and over-stressed at times, and then have nothing to do at other times. I can't follow through on plans or do what I know needs to be done.

18. **Losing Control:** I start doing things that violate my values, hurt me, and hurt those I love. As a result, I start losing respect for myself. I find excuses to miss counseling and self-help group meetings. I cut classes and push other people away by ignoring them, getting angry with them, criticizing them, or putting them down. I get so isolated that it seems like there's no one I can turn to for help. I start to feel sorry for myself and use self-pity to get attention. I feel ashamed and guilty. I know that I'm out of control, but I keep lying, using denial, and making excuses for my behavior. I feel trapped by the pain and start to believe that I'll never be able to manage my life. I see only three possible ways out—insanity, suicide, or relapse. I no longer believe that anyone or anything else can help me. No matter how hard I try to regain control, I can't do it.

19. **Thinking about Relapse:** I want to escape. I start to think that having a relapse will help me solve my problems and feel better. Things seem so bad that I start to think I might as well relapse because things couldn't get worse. I try to convince myself that I can use alcohol and drugs socially without losing control or having serious problems, even though deep inside I know that I can't. I try to put these thoughts about relapse out of my mind, but sometimes they're so strong that I can't stop them. I start to believe that relapsing is the only way to keep myself from going crazy or killing myself. Relapsing actually looks like a sane and rational alternative.

20. **Relapse:** I try to solve my problems and feel better by using alcohol or drugs. Although I rationalize my behavior, deep inside I know that alcohol and drugs won't work and will hurt me in the long run. I start using and try to control my behavior. I feel myself losing control and get disappointed because the alcohol and drugs aren't doing for me what I thought they would. My relapse spirals out of control, creating serious problems with my life and health. The problems keep getting worse until I realize that I need help and decide to try recovery one more time.

Exercise 5: Warning Sign Identification

• Part 2: Discussion Questions

Answer the following questions and be prepared to discuss your answers in your next group or individual session.

1. Pick one of the warning signs described on pages 33–36 that you identify with or have experienced in recovery.

   The warning sign I picked is:

   _____

2. The reason I picked this warning sign is: _____

   _____

3. Read the description of that warning sign again and underline the most important word or phrase. The word or phrase that I underlined is:

   _____

4. The reason I underlined this word or phrase is:

   _____

   _____

   _____

5. The way this warning sign raises my risk of having a relapse is:

   _____

   _____

   _____

   _____

Exercise 6:   Warning Sign Analysis

Instructions: Read the list of relapse warning signs again. Pick one warning sign that you identify with. Answer the following questions about it.

1.   What is the warning sign that you picked?

    _____

    _____

    _____

2.   Write a personal title for the warning sign that will be easy for you to remember. (The title shouldn't be any longer than two or three words.)

    _____

3.   Write a personal description of this warning sign. Make sure the description is a single sentence that begins with the words *I know I'm in trouble with my recovery when...* (It's important not to use any words from the personal title in the description.)

    _____

    _____

4.   When you experience this warning sign, what do you tend to think?

    _____

    _____

5.   When you experience this warning sign, what do you tend to feel, and how strong is the feeling? (You can rate the feeling on a scale of 1 to 10, with 10 being the strongest you can feel it and 1 being the weakest.)

What I tend to feel when I experience this warning sign is...	Strength of the feeling is... (1-10)

6. Check the words below that most accurately describe how you feel when the warning sign is turned on. In the blank space following each pair of feeling words rate how strong the feeling is on a scale of 1 to 10.

☐ Strong or ☐ Weak _____		☐ Safe or ☐ Threatened _____		
☐ Angry or ☐ Caring _____		☐ Fulfilled or ☐ Frustrated _____		
☐ Happy or ☐ Sad _____		☐ Proud or ☐ Ashamed, guilty _____		

7. When you experience this warning sign, what do you have an urge to do?

_____

_____

_____

8. When you experience this warning sign, what do you actually do? How is that different from what you felt an urge to do?

_____

_____

_____

9. When you do that, how do other people usually react?

_____

_____

_____

_____

Exercise 7: Situation Mapping

• Part 1: Describing a Mismanaged Situation

Instructions: Think of a particular time when you experienced this warning sign and *managed it poorly or ineffectively*. It's important to describe an experience that happened while you were **not** using alcohol and drugs.

Tell the experience as if it were a story with a beginning, a middle, and an ending. It may be helpful to start writing the story with the phrase: "This warning sign was triggered or activated when...". Describe what happened that started the whole thing. Then you can keep the story going by starting new paragraphs that begin with the phrase: "The next thing I did was...". You should end the story with a paragraph that begins with the phrase: "What finally happened was...".

If you have trouble thinking of the details of the story, ask the "who, what, when, where, and why" questions: (1) Who were you with? (2) What were you and they doing? (3) When did this happen? (4) Where did this happen? (5) Why did this happen?

Write your story in the space provided below.

The warning sign was triggered when... _____

_____

_____

_____

_____

_____

_____

_____

_____

_____

_____

_____

1. What did you want to happen as a result of your managing this situation the way you did?

_____

_____

2. Did you get what you wanted by managing the situation this way? ☐ Yes ☐ No ☐ Unsure

Please explain:

_____

_____

Exercise 7:   Situation Mapping

• Part 2: Describing an Effectively Managed Situation

Instructions: Think of a particular time when you experienced this warning sign and *managed it well or effectively*. It's important to describe an experience that happened while you were **not** using alcohol and drugs. If you can't remember managing this warning sign well, imagine how you might manage it better.

Tell the experience as if it were a story with a beginning, a middle, and an ending. It may be helpful to start writing the story with the phrase: "This warning sign was triggered or activated when…". Describe what happened that started the whole thing. Then you can keep the story going by starting new paragraphs that begin with the phrase: "The next thing I did was…". You should end the story with a paragraph that begins with the phrase: "What finally happened was…".

If you have trouble thinking of the details of the story, ask the "who, what, when, where, and why" questions: (1) Who were you with? (2) What were you and they doing? (3) When did this happen? (4) Where did this happen? (5) Why did this happen?

Write your story in the space provided below.

The warning sign was triggered when… _____

_____

_____

_____

_____

_____

_____

_____

_____

_____

_____

_____

_____

1.   What did you want to happen as a result of your managing this situation the way you did?

_____

_____

2.   Did you get what you wanted by managing the situation this way? ☐ Yes ☐ No ☐ Unsure

Please explain:

_____

_____

Exercise 8: Thought Management

• Part 1: Identifying and Clarifying the Thoughts

1. Look again at the warning sign that you picked from the warning sign list. Read the original description again.

2. What do you think people who are experiencing this warning sign would tend to think? Write these thoughts below. (Some examples would be: I'm better than you. You're better than me. I don't count. The world is unfair.)

   _____

   _____

   _____

   _____

3. Go back to the situation map you developed in Exercise 7, Part 1, and read what you wrote about the situation in which you experienced this warning sign and handled it poorly. What thoughts were you thinking in that situation? Write these thoughts below.

   _____

   _____

   _____

   _____

4. Read the thoughts you listed when you answered questions 2 and 3 above. Pick the most powerful or most important thought that someone would tend to think while experiencing this warning sign would make the situation worse instead of better. Write that thought below by completing the following statement:

   When I experience this warning sign I tend to think...

   _____

   _____

5. What does this way of thinking tell you that you **must** or **have to** think, feel, or do? (This is called a *mandate*.)

   I must...   _____

   _____

   _____

6. What do you think will happen if you **don't** do what this thought tells you that you **must** do? (This is a *threatened consequence—Do it or else!*)

   I believe that I must do what this thoughts tells me to do, or else... _____

   _____

   _____

42

7. Read the thought that you wrote in answer to question 4. What does this way of thinking tell you that you **must not** or **can't** do? (This is called an *injunction*.)

I must not... _____

_____

_____

8. What do you think will happen if you **do** what this thought tells you that you **must not** do? (This is another threatened consequence—*Don't do it or else!*)

If I do what this thought is telling me not to do, I believe the following negative thing will happen...

_____

_____

_____

Exercise 8:   Thought Management

• Part 2: Challenging Mandates and Injunctions

Review the mandates and injunctions you came up with in Part 1 of this exercise.

1.   Who taught you to think this way? Who taught you that you must do what this thought tells you to do? Write that person's name below and his or her relationship to you.

_____

2.   Is it possible that you were taught wrong? ☐ Yes ☐ No ☐ Unsure
      Please explain:

_____

_____

3.   What good things can you get out of thinking about things in this way?

_____

_____

4.   What bad things can come from thinking about things in this way?

_____

_____

5.   If you keep thinking about things in this way, what's the *best* thing that could happen?

_____

_____

6.   If you keep thinking about things in this way, what's the *worst* thing that could happen?

_____

_____

7.   If you keep thinking about things in this way, what's *most likely* to happen?

_____

_____

Exercise 8:   Thought Management

• Part 3: Identifying New Choices

1.   Read your answers to Part 1 of this exercise, looking carefully at the general thought you tend to think, what this thought tells you that you **must** do, and what it tells you that you **can't** do. Go back to the description of the situation in which you managed this warning sign *effectively.*

When you managed this warning sign effectively (or imagined yourself doing so), what did you tend to think?

_____

_____

_____

_____

_____

2.   What choices did this way of thinking give you that you didn't have when you were managing the warning sign *ineffectively*?

I can choose to... _____

_____

_____

_____

_____

3.   Go back and read the thoughts, mandates, and injunctions that you identified in Part 1. What is another way of thinking about that situation that can give you new and better choices in what you can do about it?

_____

_____

_____

_____

_____

_____

Exercise 9: Feeling Management

• Part 1: Identifying Ineffective Feeling Management Strategies

1. Read the warning sign that you picked from the warning sign list. Read the original description again.

2. What do you think people who are experiencing this warning sign would tend to feel? Write these feelings below, using "I" statements. (Some examples would be: I feel angry. I feel sad. I feel frustrated.)

    _____

    _____

    _____

    _____

3. Go back to the feelings that you wrote when you did warning sign analysis as part of Exercise 6, and write those feelings below.

    _____

    _____

4. Go back to the situation map you developed in Exercise 6, Part 1, and read the situation in which you experienced this warning sign and handled it poorly. What were you feeling in that situation? Write these feelings below, using "I" statements.

    _____

    _____

    _____

    _____

5. Use the feeling chart below to describe how you tend to feel when you're experiencing this warning sign, and how strong each feeling is.

    | ☐ Strong or ☐ Weak _____ | ☐ Safe   or ☐ Threatened _____ |
    | ☐ Angry or ☐ Caring _____ | ☐ Fulfilled or ☐ Frustrated _____ |
    | ☐ Happy or ☐ Sad _____ | ☐ Proud   or ☐ Ashamed, guilty _____ |

6. What are some of the thoughts that cause you to feel this way?

    _____

    _____

7. What are you usually doing that causes you to feel this way?

    _____

    _____

46

8. What do you usually do to try to manage these feelings?

_____

_____

9. Does the way you choose to think and act make you feel better or worse?

☐ Makes me feel better. ☐ Makes me feel worse. ☐ Doesn't change how I feel.

Why do you say that? _____

_____

_____

_____

Exercise 9:   Feeling Management

• Part 2: Learning New Feeling Management Skills

This exercise will help you look at some better feeling management skills that you can use when your warning signs are turned on. Answer these questions for the warning sign that you picked from the warning sign list.

1. How can you think ahead to situations that can trigger the kinds of strong feelings or emotions that this warning sign raises, and get ready for those situations?

    _____

    _____

    _____

    _____

2. How can you know when you start to have these strong feelings or emotions?

    _____

    _____

3. How can you stop yourself from acting on the feelings before you've had a chance to think them through? (For example, taking a few slow, deep breaths and noticing what you're feeling; calling a "time out"; getting away from the situation; or using a relaxation technique to calm the feelings down a little.)

    _____

    _____

    _____

    _____

4. How can you find words to describe what you're feeling and how strong the feelings are? (What words might you check if you used the feeling list? How would you rate the intensity of your feeling using a ten-point scale? Can you become aware of the feeling and its intensity as it's happening, by saying to yourself, "Right now I'm feeling _____ and it's OK to be feeling this way"?)

☐ Strong or ☐ Weak _____	☐ Safe or ☐ Threatened _____
☐ Angry or ☐ Caring _____	☐ Fulfilled or ☐ Frustrated _____
☐ Happy or ☐ Sad _____	☐ Proud or ☐ Ashamed, guilty _____

5. How can you figure out what you're thinking that makes you feel this way?

    _____

    _____

48

6. How can you change what you're thinking in a way that will let you feel better?

    _____

    _____

7. How can you figure out what you're doing that makes you feel this way?

    _____

    _____

8. How can you change what you're doing in a way that will let you feel better?

    _____

    _____

9. How can you notice and fight your urges to cause problems, hurt yourself, or hurt other people?

    _____

    _____

10. How can you notice when you try to avoid doing things that will help you or your situation, and force yourself to do those things even though you don't want to?

    _____

    _____

11. How can you get outside of yourself, notice what other people are feeling, and say or do something to let them know you notice their feelings and care about them?

    _____

    _____

12. Do you have a safe person you can talk to about what you're feeling? Who is that person, and what would be the best way to contact him or her?

    _____

    _____

Exercise 9: Feeling Management

• Part 3: Guidelines for Effective Feeling Management

1. I anticipate situations that are likely to bring on strong feelings and emotions.

2. I know when I'm having a strong feeling or emotion.

3. I stop myself from reacting to the feeling without thinking it through.

    A. I call a "time out" or get away from the situation for a few minutes. (Note: Excusing yourself to go to the bathroom can be helpful.)

    B. I use a relaxation technique to calm the feeling down a little.

    C. I take a deep breath and notice what I'm feeling.

4. I find words that describe what I'm feeling. I use the feeling list if necessary.

☐ Strong or	☐ Weak ___		☐ Safe	or	☐ Threatened ___
☐ Angry or	☐ Caring ___		☐ Fulfilled	or	☐ Frustrated ___
☐ Happy or	☐ Sad ___		☐ Proud	or	☐ Ashamed, guilty ___

5. I rate the intensity of the feeling using a ten-point scale.

6. I become aware of the feeling and its intensity by saying to myself, "Right now I'm feeling _____ and it's OK to be feeling this way."

7. I figure out what I'm thinking that's making me feel this way. I ask myself, "How can I change my thinking in a way that will make me feel better?"

8. I figure out what I'm doing that's making me feel this way. I ask myself, "How can I change what I'm doing in a way that will make me feel better?"

9. I become aware of urges to cause problems, hurt myself, or hurt other people and I fight those urges.

10. I become aware when I'm trying to avoid doing things that would help me or my situation, and I force myself to do those things even though I don't completely want to.

11. I get outside of myself, notice what other people are feeling, and say or do something to let them know I notice their feelings and care about them.

12. I talk with a safe person about what I'm feeling.

    • I tell them what I'm feeling and how strong the feeling is.

    • I tell them what I have an urge to do as a result of this feeling.

    • I tell them the thoughts that are making me feel this way.

    • I tell them what I'm doing that's making me feel this way.

    • I talk about how I can change what I'm thinking and doing in order to change how I feel or calm the feeling down a little.

Exercise 10: High-Risk Situation Management

1. Think of a situation you are likely to get into within the next several weeks that could make you want to use alcohol or drugs. Describe that situation below.

    _____

    _____

    _____

    _____

    _____

    _____

2. Go back to Exercise 7 and review the situation that you managed ineffectively. See if you can see a pattern or formula that you tend to use when you set yourself up to use alcohol and drugs. Describe that pattern below.

    _____

    _____

    _____

    _____

3. Now imagine that you are about to experience the high-risk situation you identified in your answer to question 1. If you were to set yourself up to justify using alcohol and drugs in that situation how would you do it? Be sure to describe the exact sequence of steps that you would take to convince yourself that "it's OK to drink and drug" or that you "have no other choice except to drink or drug." Try to think of all the steps.

    The steps I could take to convince myself to use alcohol and drugs in this situation are:

    _____

    _____

    _____

    _____

    _____

    _____

    _____

    _____

    _____

    _____

    _____

4. Go back to Exercise 7 and review the situation that you managed effectively. See if you can see a pattern or formula that you tend to use when you are able to stop yourself from using alcohol and drugs when it would be easy to do so. Describe that pattern below.

_____

_____

_____

_____

5. Go back and read your answer to question 3 which describes how you could set yourself up to use alcohol and drugs in this situation.

   A. **Intervention Point #1:** What could you have done differently near the beginning of the situation to make things come out better? (How could you have thought differently? Managed your feelings and emotions differently? Fought your self-destructive urges differently? Acted differently? Treated other people differently?)

   _____

   _____

   _____

   _____

   • If you had done these things, how would it have changed the way things turned out?

   _____

   _____

   _____

   B. **Intervention Point #2:** What could you have done differently near the middle of the situation to make things turn out better? (How could you have thought differently? Managed your feelings and emotions differently? Fought your self-destructive urges differently? Acted differently? Treated other people differently?)

   _____

   _____

   _____

   _____

   _____

   • If you had done these things, how would it have changed the way things turned out?

   _____

   _____

   _____

C. **Intervention Point #3:** What could you have done differently near the end of the situation to make things turn out better? (How could you have thought differently? Managed your feelings and emotions differently? Fought your self-destructive urges differently? Acted differently? Treated other people differently?)

_____

_____

_____

_____

_____

• If you had done these things, how would it have changed the way things turned out?

_____

_____

_____

6. **Most Important Thing Learned:** What's the most important thing you learned by doing this exercise?

_____

_____

_____

_____

7. **Future High-Risk Situation:** Is there a situation coming up in the near future that will put you at risk of experiencing this warning sign? ☐ Yes ☐ No ☐ Unsure

Please explain. _____

_____

_____

_____

8. **Application to Other High-Risk Situations:** How can you use what you learned about this situation in other high-risk situations in your life?

_____

_____

_____

_____

Exercise 11:   Recovery Planning

• Part 1: Selecting Recovery Activities

Having a plan for each day will help you recover. People who successfully recover tend to do certain basic things. These recovery principles have been proven to work. In AA, there's such a strong belief that they work, that many people with solid recovery will say, "If you want what we have, do what we did!" and, "It works if you work it!"

But not everyone in recovery does exactly the same things. Once you understand yourself and the basic principles of recovery and relapse prevention, you can build an effective personal recovery program for yourself.

When people first read the following list, they tend to get defensive. "I can't do all of those things!" they say to themselves. I invite you to think about your recovery as if you were hiking in the Grand Canyon and had to jump across a ravine that's about three feet wide and 100 feet deep. It's better to jump three feet too far than to risk jumping one inch too short. The same is true of recovery. It's better to plan to do a little bit more than you need to do, than to risk not doing enough. In AA they say, "Half measures availed us nothing!"

The seven basic recovery activities described below are actually habits of good, healthy living. Anyone who wants to live a responsible, healthy, and fulfilling life will get in the habit of regularly doing these things. People in recovery really need to do these activities, no matter what. You need a regular schedule of these activities, designed to match your own recovery needs and relapse warning signs, so your brain and your life can heal from the damage caused by addiction.

Instructions: Read the list of recovery activities below. For each numbered item, point out the activities you think will be helpful in your recovery, the obstacles that might keep you from doing them on a regular basis, and your willingness to overcome those obstacles.

1.   **Professional Counseling:** The success of your recovery will depend on your showing up regularly at recovery education sessions, group therapy sessions, and individual therapy sessions. Research studies on how well treatment works show that, the more time you spend getting professional counseling and therapy during the first two years of recovery, the more likely you are to stay in recovery.

    A.   Do I believe that I need to do this?   ☐ Yes ☐ No ☐ Unsure

    B.   The obstacles that might keep me from doing it are:

    _____

    _____

    C.   Possible ways of overcoming these obstacles are:

    _____

    _____

    D.   Will I put this on my recovery plan?   ☐ Yes ☐ No ☐ Unsure

2. **Self-Help Programs:** There are many self-help programs like Alcoholics Anonymous (AA), Narcotics Anonymous (NA), Rational Recovery, and Women For Sobriety, that can help you learn to live a sober and responsible life. These programs all have many things in common: (1) they ask you not to use **any** alcohol or drugs, and to live a responsible life; (2) they want you to go to meetings regularly, so you can meet and get to know other people who are living sober and responsible lives; (3) they ask you to meet regularly with someone who has been a regular and sober member of the group for a long time (usually called a sponsor), who will help you learn about the program and get through the rough spots; and (4) they show you a program of recovery (often in the form of steps or exercises that you work on outside of meetings) that helps you learn better ways of thinking and managing your feelings, urges, and actions. Scientific research shows that, the more committed and actively involved you are in self-help groups during the first two years of recovery, the greater your ability to avoid relapse.

   A.　Do I believe that I need to do this?　☐ Yes ☐ No ☐ Unsure

   B.　The obstacles that might keep me from doing it are:

   _____

   _____

   C.　Possible ways of overcoming these obstacles are:

   _____

   _____

   D.　Will I put this on my recovery plan?　☐ Yes ☐ No ☐ Unsure

3. **Proper Diet:** What you eat can change how you think, feel, and act. Many chemically dependent people find that they feel better if they eat three well balanced meals a day; use vitamin and amino acid (protein) supplements; avoid eating sugar and foods made with white flour; and cut back on or stop smoking cigarettes and drinking things that have caffeine, such as coffee and colas. Recovering people who don't follow these simple principles of healthy diet and meal planning tend to feel anxious and depressed, have strong and violent mood swings, feel angry and resentful all or most of the time, and sometimes have powerful cravings. They're more likely to relapse. Those who follow a healthy diet tend to feel better and have lower relapse rates.

   A.　Do I believe that I need to do this?　☐ Yes ☐ No ☐ Unsure

   B.　The obstacles that might keep me from doing it are:

   _____

   _____

   C.　Possible ways of overcoming these obstacles are:

   _____

   _____

   D.　Will I put this on my recovery plan?　☐ Yes ☐ No ☐ Unsure

4. **Exercise Program:** Doing thirty minutes of aerobic exercise each day will help your brain recover and help you feel better about yourself. Fast walking, jogging, swimming, and aerobic classes are all helpful. It's also helpful to do strength-building exercises (like weight lifting) and flexibility exercises (like stretching) along with the aerobic exercise.

   A.   Do I believe that I need to do this?   ☐ Yes ☐ No ☐ Unsure

   B.   The obstacles that might keep me from doing it are:

   _____

   _____

   C.   Possible ways of overcoming these obstacles are:

   _____

   _____

   D.   Will I put this on my recovery plan?   ☐ Yes ☐ No ☐ Unsure

5. **Stress Management Program:** Stress is a big cause of relapse. Recovering people who learn how to manage stress without using self-defeating behaviors tend to stay in recovery. Those who don't learn to manage stress tend to relapse. Stress management includes learning relaxation exercises and taking quiet time each day to relax. It also means not spending long hours working, and taking time to relax and have fun.

   A.   Do I believe that I need to do this?   ☐ Yes ☐ No ☐ Unsure

   B.   The obstacles that might keep me from doing it are:

   _____

   _____

   C.   Possible ways of overcoming these obstacles are:

   _____

   _____

   D.   Will I put this on my recovery plan?   ☐ Yes ☐ No ☐ Unsure

6. **Spiritual Development Program:** Human beings have both a physical self (based on the health of our brains and bodies) and a nonphysical self (based on the health of our value systems and spiritual lives). Most recovering people find that they need to spend time every day developing themselves spiritually (using and working on the nonphysical parts of who they are). Twelve-Step programs like AA have an excellent program for spiritual recovery, as do many communities of faith (churches, synagogues, temples, etc.) and spiritual communities. At the heart of any spiritual program are three activities: (1) fellowship, during which you spend time talking with other people who use the same kinds of methods; (2) private prayer and meditation, during which you take time alone to pray and meditate and to think about being in the presence of your higher power or think about your spiritual self; and (3) group worship, in which you pray and meditate with other people who share a spiritual philosophy like yours.

A.   Do I believe that I need to do this?   ☐ Yes ☐ No ☐ Unsure

B.   The obstacles that might keep me from doing it are:

_____

_____

C.   Possible ways of overcoming these obstacles are:

_____

_____

D.   Will I put this on my recovery plan?   ☐ Yes ☐ No ☐ Unsure

7.   **Morning and Evening Inventories:** People who successfully recover and avoid relapse learn how to stop doing self-defeating things without really being aware of what they're doing, and stop telling themselves and believing self-defeating lies about what's going on in their lives. They learn to live consciously each day, being aware of what they're doing and taking responsibility for their behavior and its consequences. To stay consciously aware, they take time each morning to plan their day (a morning planning inventory) and take time each evening to think about their progress and problems during the day (an evening review inventory). They talk about what they've learned about themselves with other people who are involved in their recovery program. These people might be their sponsors or other program friends.

A.   Do I believe that I need to do this?   ☐ Yes ☐ No ☐ Unsure

B.   The obstacles that might prevent me from doing it are:

_____

_____

C.   Possible ways of overcoming these obstacles are:

_____

_____

D.   Will I put this on my recovery plan?   ☐ Yes ☐ No ☐ Unsure

---

Exercise 11:   Recovery Planning

• Part 2: Scheduling Recovery Activities

Instructions: On the next page is a weekly planner that will help you make up a schedule of weekly recovery activities. Think of a typical week and the recovery activities you plan to do regularly. Write those activities in the correct time slot for each day. Most people find it important to have more than one scheduled recovery activity for each day.

A *recovery activity* is a particular thing you do at a scheduled time on a certain day. If there's something that you can't write on a daily planner at a specific time, then it's not a recovery activity. For example, "get more spiritually connected" wouldn't make sense on a schedule, but "spend 10 minutes meditating" would.

CENAPS® Weekly Planner

	Sunday	Monday	Tuesday	Wednesday	Thursday	Friday	Saturday
6:00 AM							
6:30 AM							
7:00 AM							
7:30 AM							
8:00 AM							
8:30 AM							
9:00 AM							
9:30 AM							
10:00 AM							
10:30 AM							
11:00 AM							
11:30 AM							
12:00 Noon							
12:30 PM							
1:00 PM							
1:30 PM							
2:00 PM							
2:30 PM							
3:00 PM							
3:30 PM							
4:00 PM							
4:30 PM							
5:00 PM							
5:30 PM							
6:00 PM							
6:30 PM							
7:00 PM							
7:30 PM							
8:00 PM							
8:30 PM							
9:00 PM							
9:30 PM							
10:00 PM							
10:30 PM							

Exercise 11: Recovery Planning

• Part 3: Testing the Schedule of Recovery Activities

1. Go back to Exercise 6: *Warning Sign Analysis* and re-read the main warning sign that you want your recovery program to help you identify and manage. Read the personal title and description and the thought, feeling, urge, and action statements carefully. What is the title and description of this warning sign?

    Title: _____

    Description: *I know I'm in trouble with my recovery when ...*

    _____

    _____

    _____

2. Read over what you've written on your CENAPS® Weekly Planner. What is *the most important* recovery activity that will help you manage this warning sign?

    _____

    A. How can you use this recovery activity to help you notice this relapse warning sign if it is turned on? (Remember, most warning signs are acted out in an automatic and unconscious way. We get "triggered," and we start using the old ways of thinking and acting without really being aware of what we're doing. To prevent relapse, it helps to regularly schedule recovery activities that will help us talk about how we're thinking, feeling, and acting, and then get feedback if our warning signs seem to be activated.)

        _____

        _____

        _____

        _____

    B. If this warning sign comes up again, how can you use this recovery activity to manage it? (Remember, "managing" a warning sign means changing how you think, feel, and act. How can this recovery activity help you feel differently? How can it help you stop thinking and doing things that make you feel like relapsing? How can it help you start thinking and doing things that make you want to get back into recovery?)

        _____

        _____

        _____

        _____

3. Review your CENAPS® Weekly Planner again. What is *the second most important* recovery activity that will help you manage this warning sign?

_____

    A.   How can you use this recovery activity to help you notice this relapse warning sign if it gets turned on?

_____

_____

_____

    B.   If this warning sign comes up for you again, how can you use this recovery activity to manage it?

_____

_____

_____

_____

4. Review your CENAPS® Weekly Planner one last time. What is *the third most important* recovery activity that will help you manage this warning sign?

_____

    A.   How can you use this recovery activity to help you notice this relapse warning sign if it gets turned on?

_____

_____

_____

    B.   If this warning sign comes up for you again, how can you use this recovery activity to manage it?

_____

_____

_____

_____

5. What other recovery activities can you think of that might be better at helping you identify and manage this warning sign if it gets turned on?

_____

_____

_____

Exercise 12:   Final Evaluation

Instructions: The real test of whether or not the exercises in this workbook have helped you will be your ability to avoid relapse. Still, it might help to look back over your work and see how well you've done. This careful evaluation can help you see areas in your Relapse Prevention Plan that need more work. By going back and finishing these areas, you might avoid relapse and the pain and problems that it causes.

Here's a checklist that can help you decide if you've learned what you needed to learn in finishing this workbook. Read each statement and ask yourself whether you've fully completed that part of the process, completed part of it, or not completed it at all. Remember: This is a self-evaluation designed to help you find out if you have the skills needed to avoid relapse. Be honest with yourself. If you relapse because you haven't learned the skills to stay in recovery, **you're** the one who will pay the price.

1.   *The Effects of Alcohol and Other Drugs:* I understand and can explain the general effects of alcohol and drugs, and the main effect that I wanted to get from alcohol and drug use.

    Level of Completion: ☐ None (0) ☐ Partial (5) ☐ Full (10)   *Score (0-10):* _____

2.   *The Decision to Start Using:* I understand and can explain the reasons why I started using alcohol or other drugs.

    Level of Completion: ☐ None (0) ☐ Partial (5) ☐ Full (10)   *Score (0-10):* _____

3.   *Alcohol and Drug-Related Problems:* I understand and can explain the problems I had because of my alcohol and drug use.

    Level of Completion: ☐ None (0) ☐ Partial (5) ☐ Full (10)   *Score (0-10):* _____

4.   *The Decision to Stop Using:* I understand and can explain the reasons why I stopped using alcohol and drugs and what I did to stay clean and sober.

    Level of Completion: ☐ None (0) ☐ Partial (5) ☐ Full (10)   *Score (0-10):* _____

5.   *Warning Sign Identification:* I can use the relapse warning sign list to find personal warning signs that lead me from solid recovery to relapse.

    Level of Completion: ☐ None (0) ☐ Partial (5) ☐ Full (10)   *Score (0-10):* _____

6.   *Warning Sign Analysis:* I've picked the most important warning sign that I've experienced; written personal titles and personal descriptions; and become aware of the thoughts, feelings, urges, and actions that make up my self-defeating responses to that warning sign.

    Level of Completion: ☐ None (0) ☐ Partial (5) ☐ Full (10)   *Score (0-10):* _____

7. **Situation Mapping:** I've described a past situation in which I managed the warning sign *badly or ineffectively,* and another past situation in which I managed the same warning sign *well or effectively.* Because I described those situations, I can explain the series of self-defeating behaviors that has kept me from effectively managing the warning sign, and another series of behaviors that has helped me manage the warning sign more effectively.

   Level of Completion: ☐ None (0) ☐ Partial (5) ☐ Full (10)   *Score (0-10):* _____

8. **Thought Management:** I've identified the main irrational thoughts that lead me from stable recovery to relapse. I can translate those thoughts into mandates (I must or have to) and injunctions (I can't or must not) and challenge my old ways of thinking. I've also found new ways of thinking that give me new and more effective choices in managing those thoughts.

   Level of Completion: ☐ None (0) ☐ Partial (5) ☐ Full (10)   *Score (0-10):* _____

9. **Feeling Management:** I've identified, found words for, and learned to communicate the unmanageable feelings that lead me from stable recovery to relapse. I've learned to take the energy that used to go into those feelings and use it in ways that won't hurt me. I can also identify new and more effective ways of managing those feelings.

   Level of Completion: ☐ None (0) ☐ Partial (5) ☐ Full (10)   *Score (0-10):* _____

10. **High-Risk Situation Management:** I've identified my high-risk situations and the critical intervention points in those situations, points where I can choose to use new behaviors that will stop the relapse process, make my recovery stronger, and help me live responsibly.

    Level of Completion: ☐ None (0) ☐ Partial (5) ☐ Full (10)   *Score (0-10):* _____

11. **Recovery Planning:** I've come up with a schedule of recovery activities that will help me keep on identifying and managing my relapse warning signs, and make it easier to get back in recovery if I do relapse.

    Level of Completion: ☐ None (0) ☐ Partial (5) ☐ Full (10)   *Score (0-10):* _____

12. **Overall Response:** I've learned to identify and manage the relapse warning signs that lead me from stable recovery to relapse, and to develop a schedule of recovery activities that help me keep identifying and managing my warning signs.

    Level of Completion: ☐ None (0) ☐ Partial (5) ☐ Full (10)   *Score (0-10):* _____

If you identified any areas where you feel you need more work, let your counselor know. Remember, it's best to be completely prepared to manage the warning signs that can lead to relapse.

Good luck on your journey of recovery!

Appendix 1:   Strategic Treatment Plan for Adolescent Warning Sign Identification and Management

THE CENAPS® CORPORATION
6147 DelTona Blvd., Spring Hill, FL 34606

352/596-8000
Fax: 352/596-8002

1.   **Problem Title:** Pattern of Chronic Relapse

2.   **Date Opened:** _____

3.   **Problem Description:** The client is unable to interrupt a pattern of chronic relapse in spite of previous attempts at recovery or the client is fearful that he or she might relapse in spite of making a commitment not to.

4.   **Goal:** The client will be able to interrupt this pattern of chronic relapse by learning how to identify and manage relapse warning signs, and how to develop a recovery program that supports ongoing warning sign identification and management.

5.   **Interventions:** The client will participate in a combination of group and individual therapy sessions, psychoeducational sessions, supervised study halls, and self-help group meetings, in which the following interventions will be implemented:

   (1)   **The Effects of Alcohol and Other Drugs:** The client will understand and be able to explain the general effects of alcohol and drugs and the primary effect that he or she wanted to get from alcohol and drug use.

   (2)   **The Decision to Start Using:** The client will understand and be able to explain the reasons why he or she started using alcohol or other drugs.

   (3)   **Alcohol- and Drug-Related Problems:** The client will understand and be able to explain the problems he or she experienced as a result of his or her alcohol and drug use.

   (4)   **The Decision to Stop Using:** The client will understand and be able to explain the reasons why he or she stopped using alcohol and drugs and what he or she did to stay clean and sober.

   (5)   **Warning Sign Identification:** The client will review a list of common relapse warning signs and identify a personal warning sign that leads from stable recovery to relapse.

   (6)   **Warning Sign Analysis:** The client will analyze the selected warning sign by writing a personal title and description; and by identifying the irrational thoughts, unmanageable feelings, self-destructive urges, and self-defeating behaviors associated with that warning sign.

   (7)   **Situation Mapping:** The client will describe one past situation in which he or she experienced this warning sign in recovery and managed it poorly. This situation will be used to identify the self-reinforcing problem structure that drives the relapse process. The client will then be asked to identify one past situation in which he or she experienced this warning sign in recovery and managed it effectively. This situation will be used to identify the basic solution structure that will become the foundation for warning sign management and recovery planning.

(8) **Thought Management:** The client will identify the irrational thoughts that drive the identified relapse warning sign and develop new and more effective ways of thinking that will help him or her avoid relapse.

(9) **Feeling Management:** The client will identify the unmanageable feelings that drive the identified relapse warning sign and develop new and more effective ways of managing those feelings that will help him or her avoid relapse.

(10) **Behavior and Situation Management:** The client will identify the high-risk situations and self-defeating behaviors that drive the identified relapse warning sign. The client will learn to manage high-risk situations more effectively by identifying three intervention points where he or she can use more effective ways of thinking, feeling, and acting to avoid relapse. The client will apply these new ways of coping to a future high-risk situation.

(11) **Recovery Planning:** The client will develop a schedule of recovery activities that will support the ongoing identification and management of relapse warning signs. The client will identify how each recovery activity can be adapted to help him or her identify and manage the critical relapse warning sign.

6. **Date Closed:** _____

7. **Description of Outcome:** At the completion of Relapse Prevention Therapy, the client's ability to use the skills related to each step of the relapse prevention intervention is as follows:

(1) *The Effects of Alcohol and Other Drugs:* The client understands and is able to explain the general effects of alcohol and drugs and the primary effect that he or she desired from alcohol and drug use.

Level of Completion: ☐ Full ☐ Partial ☐ None

(2) *The Decision to Start Using:* The client understands and is able to explain the reasons why he or she started using alcohol or other drugs.

Level of Completion: ☐ Full ☐ Partial ☐ None

(3) *Alcohol and Drug-Related Problems:* The client understands and is able to explain the problems he or she experienced as a result of alcohol and drug use.

Level of Completion: ☐ Full ☐ Partial ☐ None

(4) *The Decision to Stop Using:* The client understands and is able to explain his or her reasons for stopping alcohol and drug use and what he or she did to stay clean and sober.

Level of Completion: ☐ Full ☐ Partial ☐ None

(5) *Warning Sign Identification:* The client has successfully used a relapse warning sign list to identify personal warning signs that lead from stable recovery to relapse.

Level of Completion: ☐ Full ☐ Partial ☐ None

(6) **Warning Sign Analysis:** The client has selected one or more warning signs that he or she has experienced and has written personal titles, personal descriptions, and thought, feeling, urge, and action statements that clearly describe the self-defeating responses in these warning signs.

Level of Completion: ☐ Full ☐ Partial ☐ None

(7) **Situation Mapping:** The client has objectively described a past situation in which the warning sign was *ineffectively* managed, a past situation in which the warning sign was *effectively* managed, the self-defeating behaviors that prevented effective management, and self-enhancing behaviors that can be used for effective warning sign management.

Level of Completion: ☐ Full ☐ Partial ☐ None

(8) **Thought Management:** The client has identified the primary irrational thoughts that lead from stable recovery to relapse and the irrational mandates and injunctions that drive those thoughts, has challenged the old ways of thinking, and has developed new ways of thinking that provide new and more effective choices.

Level of Completion: ☐ Full ☐ Partial ☐ None

(9) **Feeling Management:** The client has identified, labeled, and learned to communicate and redirect energy from the unmanageable feelings that lead to relapse. The client can also identify new and more effective ways of managing those feelings.

Level of Completion: ☐ Full ☐ Partial ☐ None

(10) **Behavior and Situation Management:** The client has identified high-risk situations and critical intervention points in those situations in which he or she can choose to use behaviors that will interrupt the relapse and reinforce recovery.

Level of Completion: ☐ Full ☐ Partial ☐ None

(11) **Recovery Planning:** The client has identified a schedule of recovery activities that will support the ongoing identification and management of relapse warning signs and support early intervention should relapse occur.

Level of Completion: ☐ Full ☐ Partial ☐ None

(12) **Overall Response:** The client has developed the overall ability to identify and manage relapse warning signs and to develop a schedule of recovery activities that supports ongoing warning sign identification and management.

Level of Completion: ☐ Full ☐ Partial ☐ None

Appendix 2:   Additional Resources

Terence T. Gorski and The CENAPS® Corporation have developed a core technology package for relapse prevention. This new package is designed to meet the needs of cost containment while providing effective and high-integrity approaches to treatment. The components of this new core technology package are released as *The Brief Therapy for Relapse Prevention Series*. This series maintains the same principles that have made Relapse Prevention Therapy a preferred approach for the chemical dependency field. It simplifies and streamlines the procedures and extends them to the treatment of mental and personality disorders.

The Brief Therapy for Relapse Prevention Series contains two relapse prevention workbooks: *The Relapse Prevention Counseling* Workbook and *The Relapse Prevention Therapy Workbook*. Both workbooks are targeted, strategic, and effective. Both allow you to identify the critical relapse warning signs that lead from stable recovery to relapse; and to identify and manage the irrational thoughts, unmanageable feelings, self-destructive urges, and self-defeating behaviors that drive these relapse warning signs. You should be aware of some differences between the two workbooks.

The Relapse Prevention Counseling Workbook presents seven powerful clinical processes designed to identify a key or critical warning sign quickly and teach clients to manage the irrational thoughts, unmanageable feelings, and self-destructive urges that drive that warning sign. This workbook presents a *counseling process* that is most appropriate for people in early recovery who have a clearly identified warning sign or high-risk situation. The process can usually be completed in between seven and fourteen sessions.

The Relapse Prevention Therapy Workbook presents fifteen core processes that are divided into five sections: stabilization, assessment, warning sign identification, warning sign management, and recovery planning. This workbook presents a *psychotherapy process* that relates current warning signs to the core dynamics of personality that drive them. As a result, it is most appropriate for clients with a stable recovery who are willing and able to examine childhood patterns and relate those patterns to the problem of relapse. This process is more involved than simple warning sign identification and management and can usually be completed in between fifteen and thirty sessions dependent upon the severity of the problems that are identified during the process.

In brief, *The Relapse Prevention Counseling Workbook* is a quick and easy way to identify and clarify immediate problems that threaten recovery. *The Relapse Prevention Therapy Workbook* is ideal for people who want to go in depth by identifying the core personality-driven patterns that repeatedly compel them into the self-defeating behaviors that lead to relapse.

In addition, Terence T. Gorski's Relapse Prevention Core Technology Package offers a variety of materials for clinicians and recovering people. These include:

- *Staying Sober: A Guide for Relapse Prevention,* the world-renowned, easy-to-read book on addiction, recovery, and relapse prevention. (Available in English, Spanish, and Polish.)

- *The Staying Sober Workbook,* the classic companion workbook to *Staying Sober.* (Available in English and Spanish.)

- *How to Start Relapse Prevention Support Groups,* a must for recovering people and therapists who want to strengthen recovery with a time-proven self-help format. (Available in English and Spanish.)

- *The Phases and Warning Signs of Relapse,* a handy pamphlet that provides at-a-glance descriptions that can help stop relapse before it happens. (Available in English and Spanish, and on audiotape.)

- The *Staying Sober Recovery Education Modules,* a comprehensive, ready-to-use, highly adaptable professional education program for recovery and relapse prevention.

- *The Recovery and Relapse Videotape Series*, a powerful set of lectures that supports the recovery education process. These are ideal for clients who have limited access to in-person sessions. (Also available in low-cost audiotapes.)

These and many other materials are available from Herald House/Independence Press, P.O. Box 390, Independence, MO 64051-0390, 1-800-767-8181. For information about training and consultation, or to find a Certified Relapse Prevention Specialist in your area, call or write to The CENAPS® Corporation, 6147 Deltona Blvd, Spring Hill, FL 34606, 352/596-8000